First published in Great Britain in 1991
by Marshall Pickering

Marshall Pickering is an imprint of
HarperCollinsReligious
Part of HarperCollins Publishers
77–85 Fulham Palace Road, London W6 8JB

A catalogue record for this book is
available from the British Library

Printed and bound in Hong Kong

WINEBIBBER

THE
BIG
HOLY ONE

A compilation from the Winebibber comic, issues 1 to 7

by Mike Brooks and Mike Stonelake

With special thanks to:

Brett Jordan & Impression Litho

George Eckford & Hans Willem

Christine Kirkham

Charles Schnitzenhausenhesenhosengrüben

Teenage Mutant Christians courtesy Strait Magazine

Midnight Caller, Humphrey the Easter Egg, The Punk Samaritan and *Prodigal Pig*

courtesy Plus (Challenge Literature Fellowship)

Wayne Baribondo and his Dancing Slippers

One of the *Rev. Ken Doddle* cartoons drawn by Simes (see if you can guess which one)

WINEBIBBER

INTRODUCTION
A History of the Winebibber

The origin of the works of Winebibber remain one of the Great Mysteries of the Western Church. Leading scholars attribute the original cartoon works to an order of ninth century monks, called the Winebibbers.

This band of renegade monks were so nick-named because of their excessively silly behaviour, which caused many to label them drunkards. Banished from their Monastery for the crime of laughing during their quiet times, it appears the Monkish scribes sought shelter in a cave in Scotland, where they worked day and night completing their first volume of illuminated cartoon manuscripts. The rapturous response was overwhelming, and further volumes were to follow.

This was a happy time in the history of Winebibber. The common folk enjoyed the wit and mirth of the highly talented monks, and in return provided the monks with food and clothing, and fresh ink for their quills.

This idyllic phase was not to last, however. And, as is so often the case with any daring new form of art, the Church authorities of the day decided the popular monks were a threat to their position of power and, once again, the monks were banished.

Rev. Flourier, chuckling over a copy of the Winebibber.

This time, unfortunately, the monks were split up and sent in separate directions, and no more of the cartoons were to appear. The humorous volumes were confiscated, and were locked away in the church safe. Here they were to remain until the mid-sixteenth century and the time of the Great Reformation.

Whilst Luther and contemporaries sought to re-introduce the neglected doctrine of salvation by faith alone, a revival of a quite different nature was taking place on the tiny isle of Duffledorf, off the coast of Belgium.

Reverend Flourier, a recent convert and the new vicar of Duffledorf Cathedral, stumbled across a long forgotten collection of humorous sketchings in the church cellar, whilst spring cleaning. The effect of mirth upon him was so overwhelming that he apparently ran through the streets exclaiming, "At last a comic in all its fullness!" He had, of course rediscovered the golden works of Winebibber.

Immediately Flourier put the books on public display and reintroduced the neglected doctrine of humour by faith alone; starting with the famous precept, "I read the Winebibber, therefore I laugh." Again, the Church authorities were alerted to the revival of humour and, once more, the Winebibber was taken from the people, and its perpetrator banished. And so things were to remain in darkest solemnity for another five hundred years.

It was not until three years ago, in September 1987, at Lancashire Polytechnic, in Preston, that the Winebibber once more made its appearance. The long lost scrolls were found lurking in a dim and dank student's cellar. Experts immediately started work preparing the world's first complete facsimile of The Big Holy One – the works of Winebibber, which we present here in their complete unabridged form.

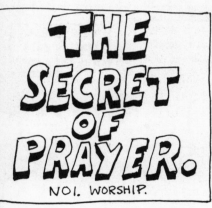

LETTERBOX

Amplified Bible

May I recommend (invite, suggest, propose, warmly commend) that any keen readers (scholars, students, intellectually - orientated people) might prosper (benefit, gain) from a careful study (inspection, investigation, analysis) of the Amplified Bible (bible).

S. Jackson
Yorkshire

Luminous Cartoons

Did you know that Winebibber Cartoons are luminous in the long dark night of the soul?

M. Lance
Middlesex

Tired of Turkey?

If you're tired of Turkey every Christmas then why not go back 2000 years and savour the original flavour of Galilee – fish.

P. Johnson
Birmingham

Fish!

Yesterday I went into a fishmongers and asked for a fish, but he gave me a snake. I'm glad God's not like that.

Paul Stockley
Cambridge

Why not tell us about your fishy frolics? There's ten pounds for the best one

May I say how much I enjoyed your recent feature on women's lingerie. I personally enjoy wearing... oh, sorry, wrong magazine.

Mr. David Coppel
Brighton

Miracle

Last night our family sat down eagerly to our usual Tuesday night feast of haddock and chips. We closed our eyes to say grace only to reopen them and discover the table now piled high with fish. Who said miracles don't happen any more?

J. Smith
Gerrards Cross

Fish

Last night my son came home having stopped out 3 days and nights. I was worried sick. All he could say was that he'd spent his time in the belly of a large fish. I gave him a good clout around the ear and sent him to bed with no supper.

Jonah's mother
Jerusalem

Rule over the fish

I have decided to take Gen.1 v 28 seriously, "RULE over the fish of the sea ". However, some fish are very difficult to measure because they are so slippery.

M. Paisley
Liverpool

Fish of the month

Thank you to Ian Harris of Chelmsford for suggesting this month's fish of the month – Trout.

Come on readers, what's your favourite fish? Write and tell us and we'll give a prize to the best fish we receive.

Spot the Difference

Which man has been Born Again?

Fish-Puzzle

Which disciple has caught the fish with the 4 Drachma coin in it s mouth?

MUSIC CORNER
RECORD OF THE MONTH
I Just Want To March Up And Down
The Salvation Army

Army fans won't be disappointed by this brand new LP by one of the worlds oldest groups. This Album is sheer quality, from the opening track, "Running on the Spot", to the final "Quick March", in which boots crunch in perfect stereo effect. "Collection Boxes" is a live recording made at the regular Saturday Charity appeal from Brighton City Centre. "Polishing Boots" is so good you can almost smell the polish. There is also an excellent solo by Corporal T. Wood, "Running to the Shops to Get Some Milk". And if you're still not satisfied, we hear that the next LP will be featuring musical instruments. ★★★
Paul Williams

CLIFF RICHARD IS A CHRISTIAN

The Winebibber can exclusively reveal that the famous Pop singer, Cliff Richard has become a Christian. He became a Christian twenty years ago, and his song "You, me and Jesus" is about Jesus.
Matt Smith

Cliff Richard

nuns 'n' monks

It was the day before the annual nuns v. monks rugby match. The monks were training hard, hoping to beat the nuns for the first time in five years.

But meanwhile......

Next day at the match......

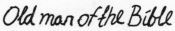

THE not so DIVINE REVELATIONS of brother HENRY

My visions described the trinity. My first occurred at 3 AM, June 3rd, 1988.

I awoke with a painful emptiness in my stomach and a picture of rice pudding in my head.

At first I dismissed this picture, but it did not go away. So I went to the kitchen....

Soon I found myself cooking and eating rice pudding. Suddenly the meaning of the vision was clear.

Skin = Holy Spirit

Big Jam blob = Son

Actual rice pudding bit = Father.

The following day ran as usual; breakfast, off to work, elevensies, dinner.

At 3 PM, precisely 12 hours after my first vision, I began to feel peckish. My thoughts turned to the snack machine.

At that moment I received my second vision. A chocolate bar I had never seen before.

Caramel = Father

Nougat = Son

Wafer = Holy Spirit

What a blessing! — My second vision concerning the trinity.

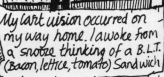

My last vision occurred on my way home. I awoke from a snooze thinking of a B.L.T. (Bacon, lettuce, tomato) Sandwich

Amazingly, one lay on the seat next to me on the train.

However, further investigation was interrupted by a blinding flash, which I attributed to a lack of faith and not the angry owner of the aforementioned sandwich.

Wish you were here...

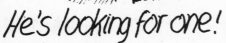

He's looking for one!

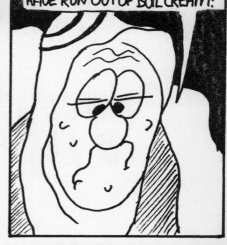

Bible Verse Dot to Dot.©

Join the Dots and Discover what the Bible verse below is.

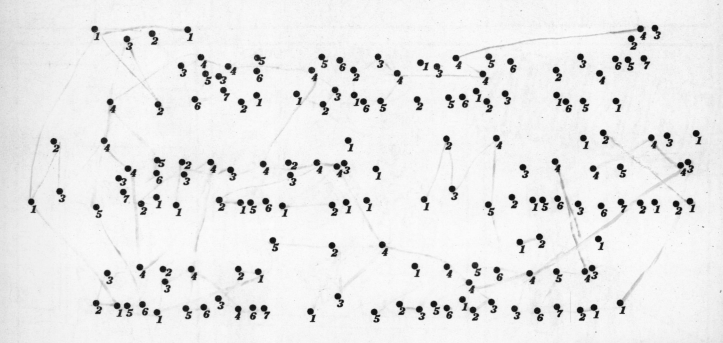

GORDON BEWS
OUT OF THE
Good News

KEVIN
BUMBLE
he's so humble

COAT PIG

THE BIG BOOM THEORY OF CREATION

Flat Feet

One
night I had a
dream. I was walking
along the beach by myself
when I noticed I was only wearing
one flip-flop. I looked back and
noticed it had come off in the sand. I
turned to go back and fetch it but at
that moment a big wave came along and
swept my flip-flop into the sea. It
wouldn't have been so bad but I'd
'borrowed' them from my sister without
asking. Fortunately though it didn't
go too far out, so I went to get it.
Soon I noticed I was walking
in quicksand and I was
beginning to sink. I tried
to turn around but by
now the sand was up to
my ankles and I fell over
face first. Amazingly my
hand fell onto the flip-flop
and I managed to struggle to
my feet with it. I was just
starting to cheer up when a
dog ran up and bit it in two.
Rats. When I got home my
mum told me off for missing
my tea and I now owe
my sister £2.50.
Boo Hoo.

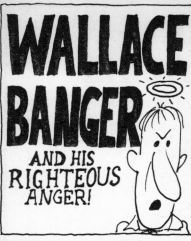

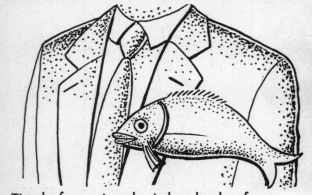

ROBIN MIRE

He's not on fire

Gordon Bewes EPISTLE BOX

Potatoes

On bonfire night I ate 20 hot potatoes. Is this a sin?

R. Mustow
Preston

Sermon

I have thought up 101 dull things to do during an interesting sermon.

P. Langston
Preston

Highlighter Pen

On "March for Jesus" day I picked up a green highlighter pen. If anyone has lost one, please contact me through the Winebibber.

D. Fenn
Preston

Thing!

I have prepared 101 dull sermons to preach during an interesting thing.

T. Griffiths
Preston

Read

I usually take a copy of 101 dalmations to read during a boring sermon.

C. Duddy
Preston

Sin?

I can only think of 100 things to do during a dull sermon. Is this a sin?

H. Sharrard
Preston

Big Top

At Greenbelt I lost a big top. Can anyone help?

Chairman of Greenbelt
Preston

Green !!

Has anyone lost a green highlighter potato during a boring sermon? Please contact me through the Winebibber

D. Preston
Nottingham

Green Belt

At the Big Top I lost a green belt. Can anyone help?

Vice-chairman of Greenbelt
Preston

Behemoth

Thank you to Mark Ellery of Preston for suggesting this month's Behemoth of the month – Belinda the Behemoth.

Come on readers, tell us about your favourite Behemoth? Write and tell us and we'll give a prize to the best Behemoth letter we receive.
–G.B.

Autographs

I have recently started collecting the autographs of vicars on the inside covers of my bible. So far I have 101!

A. Smethurst
Preston

Disciples

Q. Why did Jesus have 12 disciples?
A. One for each month of the year!

M. Ivory
Preston

Bookstall

Have you noticed that Church bookstalls are getting bigger and bigger, and stocking new ranges and products all the time? I don't go along on Sunday to worship anymore, I go to worSHOP!

S. Walton
Preston

Worship

Worship? It should be called worshop. I used to be handed a hymn book and a Bible when I went into church. Now I'm handed a shopping basket!

N. Perera
Preston

Bookstall

Our church bookstall has started selling food and clothes and all sorts of things. I was commenting on this to my vicar at the check out counter just last week. He joked that he didn't go to church anymore, he went to worshop!

D. Rankin
Preston

Bumped

Last week I bumped into my vicar in the local supermarket. He was raising his food in the air, and banging his tins of baked beans together. I asked him what he was doing and he said he was "Worshopping!"

T. Mulholland
Preston

Supermarket

Our local supermarket is certainly good value for money. If you rent a hymn book you get a free communion thrown in free!

M. Sloane
Preston

Sunday

Last Sunday I practised putting on the local green with a friend. Worship! It should be called golf.

K. Turner
Preston

SNEDRICK MARCH SONGSHEET

Just Really Music 1989

Intro to "I want to skip"

Leader: Make way, make way
All: Make way, make way
Leader: For the fuzzy of fuzzies
All: And the warm of warms
Leader: We just want to skip and dance
All: And run and prance
Leader: But sometimes...
All: We just want to sit prayerfully

I want to skip for you
I want to skip for you.
I want to leap and really prance about
I need a trampoline
I need a trampoline
I am going to scream
And really yell and shout.

Snedrick 1989

March starts

Intro to "Clapping"

Leader: We raise our banners
All: And wave our balloons
Leader: Some of them are red
All: And some of them are blue
Leader: We just want to blow and blow
All: And blow them up for you

Clapping, swaying, moving about
Jumping up and down without a doubt
We're getting all worked up
And we're feeling all warm and gooey
And what's more, the service hasn't even
                          started.

Snedrick 1989

Marchers get into shapes off no less than 9
sides (all angles must be equal), and pray.
Note: Stewards will be on hand with protractors.

Eugh what's that feeling
Spreading through my body
It's started in my stomach
And is rising through my body
And it feels...
And it feels...
And it feels...
Warm and fuzzy.

Snedrick 1989

Marchers form human pyramids and raise your
hands by faith.

Intro to "We just really"

Leader: Rattle those tambourines
All: We're rattling them already
Leader: Well rattle them some more
All: We can't!, we can't!

We just really want to praise you
We really just honestly really do
We'll raise our feet to you
And we'll feel all warm and fuzzy
And satisfied
And really really peaceful.

Snedrick 1989

THE SECRET OF PRAYER
No.3
Using the Right Words

"CHUR

The cut-out bo

Who killed the church mouse

Rev. Green

Deacon Blue

Bishop Burnt Umber

Su
Te

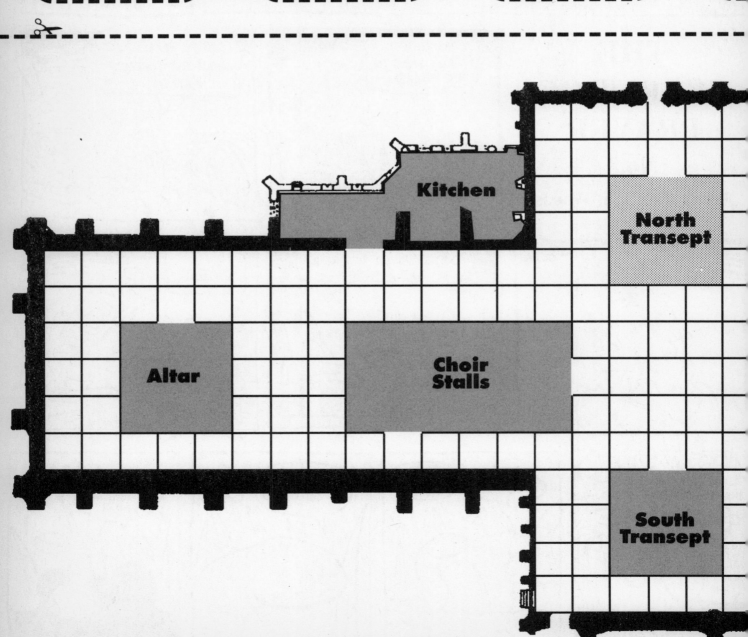

CHO"

game
here and with what?

School Scarlet

House group Leader Mustard

Church Cat

Candlestick

Collection Plate

Bell Rope

Hymn Book

Bible

Mouse Trap

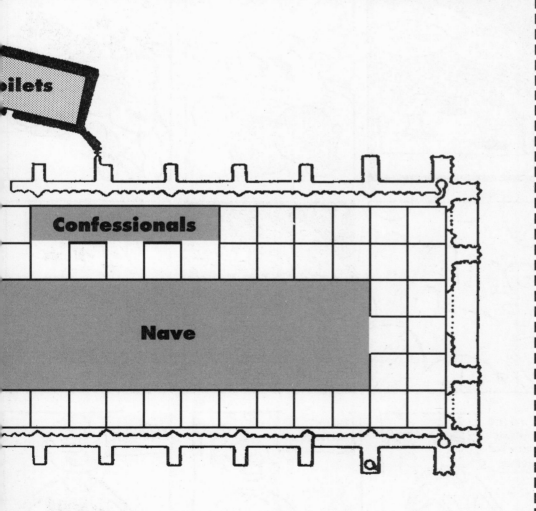

Toilets

Confessionals

Nave

GORDON BEWES

HE'S STILL OUT OF THE
GOOD NEWS

THE SECRET OF PRAYER

No. 5

Prayer during everyday tasks

BILL GRIMM'S PROGRESS

ROBIN MIRE

He's still not on fire

COMMENTATOR'S CORNER

A Winebibber study in Adrian Snail.

by Rev. Slug Baxter

Let us don our wellington boots and boldly venture into the jolly green world of Adrian Snail. Here, amongst the vegetables and flowers, the grass and the trees, is the setting in which we will consider the philosophical writings of Adrian Snail. Do not be like the sceptics who travel the wide garden path which ends up in the compost heap. But instead, take up your shell and discover the deep truths of Adrian.

Have we not all at sometime asked, like the snail, "what is the meaning of life?" The original snailish is clearer, "just what exactly is the flipping meaning of life, anyhow?" The force of the question demands a response. So what can we learn from the response of Adrian? I believe two things. Firstly, he is prepared to devote his full time and attention to the given task, and secondly, he does not refrain from using facial contortions. "What's that!", I hear some exclaim, "facial contortions". Yes, we do not find any support for the view that facial contortions are unwinebibberical. Nor, however, can we agree with facial expressionists who claim we can answer all of life's questions by pulling faces alone. In Adrian we find a balance between the two.

And what is the result of these ponderings? The text is not ambiguous, but is clear and decisive – "eating cabbage". Note Adrian does not say "cabbage" but "eating cabbage". It is not enough merely to look at the cabbage, smell the cabbage or even to talk to the cabbage. Many are like this , they may even know the cabbage creed off by heart, but this is also missing the point. **It is the actual consumption of cabbage which is all important.** Mode does not matter. Pickled, boiled or raw, each has it's place. So let us take large bites and chew fully so that our digestion may be complete. And where exactly is the cabbage? Well, in a sense, the cabbage is everywhere. In fact, in a metaphysical sense, we are the cabbage.

The Rev. Slug Baxter is a professor of horticultural theology at Sunny Lanes Nursery, Devon. He has written several books. His new title due in the spring is entitled "I hear the sound of cabbage leaves in the trees"

SALLY ARMSTRONG

EVANGELIST to THE (un)KNOWN UNIVERSE

THE

BOOK

SHOP

THE
SECRET OF
PRAYER
No.4

Speaking in Tongues

Winebibber prayer cards
"a snigger in times of despair"

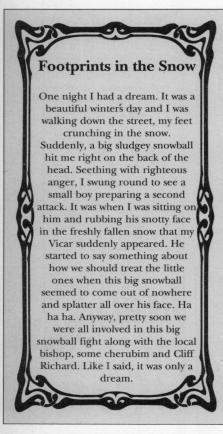

Footprints in the Snow

One night I had a dream. It was a beautiful winter's day and I was walking down the street, my feet crunching in the snow. Suddenly, a big sludgey snowball hit me right on the back of the head. Seething with righteous anger, I swung round to see a small boy preparing a second attack. It was when I was sitting on him and rubbing his snotty face in the freshly fallen snow that my Vicar suddenly appeared. He started to say something about how we should treat the little ones when this big snowball seemed to come out of nowhere and splatter all over his face. Ha ha ha. Anyway, pretty soon we were all involved in this big snowball fight along with the local bishop, some cherubim and Cliff Richard. Like I said, it was only a dream.

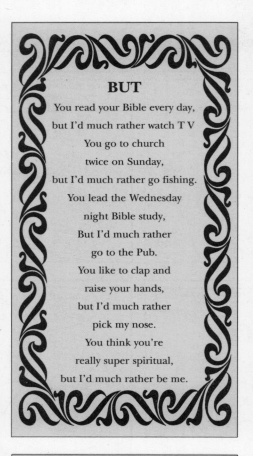

BUT

You read your Bible every day,
but I'd much rather watch T V
You go to church
twice on Sunday,
but I'd much rather go fishing.
You lead the Wednesday
night Bible study,
But I'd much rather
go to the Pub.
You like to clap and
raise your hands,
but I'd much rather
pick my nose.
You think you're
really super spiritual,
but I'd much rather be me.

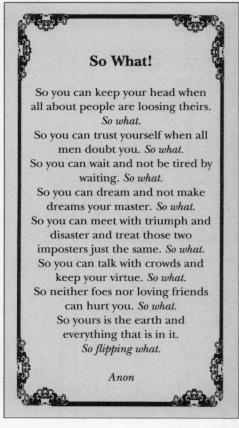

So What!

So you can keep your head when all about people are loosing theirs. *So what.*
So you can trust yourself when all men doubt you. *So what.*
So you can wait and not be tired by waiting. *So what.*
So you can dream and not make dreams your master. *So what.*
So you can meet with triumph and disaster and treat those two imposters just the same. *So what.*
So you can talk with crowds and keep your virtue. *So what.*
So neither foes nor loving friends can hurt you. *So what.*
So yours is the earth and everything that is in it.
So flipping what.

Anon

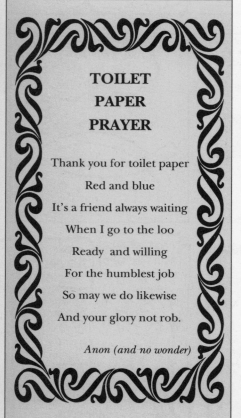

TOILET PAPER PRAYER

Thank you for toilet paper

Red and blue

It's a friend always waiting

When I go to the loo

Ready and willing

For the humblest job

So may we do likewise

And your glory not rob.

Anon (and no wonder)

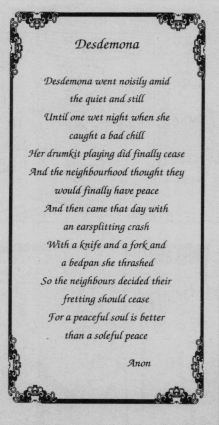

Desdemona

*Desdemona went noisily amid
the quiet and still
Until one wet night when she
caught a bad chill
Her drumkit playing did finally cease
And the neighbourhood thought they
would finally have peace
And then came that day with
an earsplitting crash
With a knife and a fork and
a bedpan she thrashed
So the neighbours decided their
fretting should cease
For a peaceful soul is better
than a soleful peace*

Anon

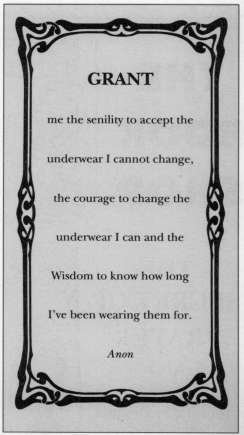

GRANT

me the senility to accept the

underwear I cannot change,

the courage to change the

underwear I can and the

Wisdom to know how long

I've been wearing them for.

Anon

GORDON BEWES

OUT OF THE
GOOD NEWS

WHEN DINOSAURS ROAMED THE EARTH

The Snowvicar

On December 6th last year, mild mannered church-goer Terry Ogden had an experience he'll never forget...

Layman Harry White was a strictly hands-down Christian until one day...

Thankfully Harry survived, it was a false alarm. Terry wasn't so lucky. Be warned, next time it could be you.

RECIPE CORNER

FISH AND BREAD SURPRISE

INGREDIENTS

5 loaves
2 small fishes
salt and pepper (optional).

This tasty snack should serve between 4000 and 5000 men, not including women and children. Even the fussiest palate will be satisfied by this quick and easy to prepare meal. To cook, simply look up to heaven and hold the bread, gently but firmly between the thumb and forefinger. Next, tear the bread into small lumps measuring approximately 2 millicubits square whilst giving thanks.
Thanks should be given for between 2 to 3 minutes.
A miraculous meal in minutes, with enough left
over to fill 12 baskets.

Robin Mire in
SIGNS AND WONDERS

GORDON BEWES EPISTLE PAGE

Funny Food

My mother cooks very funny food, we can't stop laughing when we eat it.

G. Eckford
High Wycombe

Why Scarf?

My grandmother recently knitted me some Y-fronts for Christmas. However they were a bit too big so I wear them around my neck. I call it a Y-scarf.

G Butt
Northwood

Music Joke

My friend can play musical jokes. Here is one of them:

G. Chapman
S Ruislip

Joke

Some people laugh at jokes, but I dance instead. If someone tells a good joke I do a little jig or maybe a foxtrot.

S. Tate
Ruislip

Amusing!!

Some people laugh at food, but I find humour quite amusing.

S. Thomas
Ruislip

Holy Hornby's

After hearing about the recent "Bike for Bibles" campaign, I decided to use my own hobby to spread God's Word. As a member of the Chistleworth Valley Model Railway Club, I have started my "Trains for Testaments" campaign. My first project was to send a Bible to John, the controller at Chudbury Junction. I sellotaped it to a pullman coach and sent it down the line. Unfortunately it was too big to go under the bridge, and demolished it completely, along with a signal box and most of Chudbury Junction. Since then I have been kicked out of the club! Talk about persecution.

M. Thornton
Northwood

Dancing

I like dancing, but not to music. Sometimes I put on a blank tape and just freak out. I also like dancing to pneumatic drills. My friends buy 12 inch records to dance to, but I dance to 12 inch rulers.

Dotty the Cat
Manchester

Souffle

Recently I bought one of Delia Sniff's cookery books thinking it was one of her books on prayer. However I did make a very nice souffle during my quiet-time.

P. Jordan
Ruislip Manor

The Winebibber denies all accusations that our last issue contained backwards writing. Claims that the Winebibber contained the word **WINEBI666ER** written backwards are totally untrue.

Ed

Witness of the Week

A carefully positioned wall (Praise March) effectively blocked Mr Henry's (H) exit from the shopping arcade, enabling the All Saints successful twin attack,

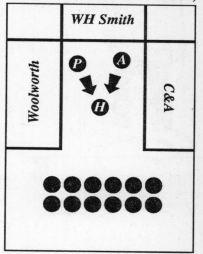

Alan (A) and Peggy (P), plenty of opportunity to deliver tracts and testimonies. Mr Henry was finally allowed to go when he had signed up for a 'Just Looking' Group.

Classifieds

HOLY GHOSTBUSTERS

THE FAMILY BONGS
THEY SPEAK IN TONGUES

GIDEON

West End Presentations

OXFORD RD.
987 5435

HEYMARKET
654 7621

PRESTON POLY
C.U. video-nite

TEENAGE MUTANT NINJA BIBLES

Sneeker has stolen Herbert's third year dissertation on the soteriology of Mark. Can the Ninja Bibles return it in time for the End of Term Dance? And who is that man in the argyle sweater.

The Prophetic Story of St. John on the Isle of Patmos...

Apocalypse Soon

Starring the Locusts of Iron as the Helicopters

CHELSEA
863 5422/9877

GREAT NEW SAMSON SEASON COMING SOON! Watch your favourite Bible strongman in an exciting new season of classic oldies.

SAMSON FIRST BLOOD

SAMSON 2,3,4 & 5
(Quadruple bill)
SAMSON
Verses Godzilla
SAMSON
in Outer Space
SAMSON
& the Great Theological Disaster
Sep Progs. 1.30, 3.45, 8.20
Late show Fri & Sat. 11pm

Just when you thought it was safe to read your Bible

JONAH

Who framed

LARRY LEVIATHAN

Starring
Blob Hoskins

Sep Progs. 1.30, 3.45, 8.20
Late show Fri & Sat. 11pm

FULHAM
644 9898/6555

LAST EXIT TO UGUDUGU
↓ ↓

IN DOLBY STEREO

Sep Progs. 1.30, 3.45, 8.20
Late show Fri & Sat. 11pm

BIBLE WARS

Inter-Galactic Seminary invites Theologon to a prayer meeting, secretly planning to steal his real leather-look bible of which they are jealous. Can Weslex save the day? Heavy duty theological action from the makers of Heresy from Planet Bongo.

PUDLEY Y.P.F.
654 7621

KUNG BIBLE-FU

Great Chinese theological action. Bruce Bib-Lee can't wait to get home to try out his new electronic Bible, but Norman, the Christian Union president, has other ideas. **Special guest appearance by Hudson Taylor.**

Sep Progs. 1.30, 3.45, 8.20
Late show Fri & Sat. 11pm

The 39 Articles

George Whitfield and Johnny Wesley star in this fast-moving comedy about the Great English Revival. Watch out for a hilarious car chase at the end.

Charlie and the Bible Factory

There are only 5 golden tickets to visit Billy Bonka's Bible Factory and Charlie has got one. But who is that man in the argyle sweater?

Three Wise Men and a Baby

There are only 5 golden tickets left for the End of Term Dance, but who is that man in the waterproof argyle slippers? Intense Psych-drama starring Samson as the King of Planet Bongo.

PROGRAMMES MAY BE SUBJECT TO ALTERATION

can men and women be friends or...

does gleaning always get in the way?

when Ruth met Boaz...

TOWERING INFERNO OF BABEL

Sep Progs. 1.30, 3.45, 8.20
Late show Fri & Sat. 11pm

RAIDERS
OF THE LOST BEHEMOTH

STARRING
Harrison Ford Transit
Special Guest Appearance by Wayne Baribondo and his Dancing Slippers

BIBLE REPAIR MAN

A TIME OF CROAKING!

INTRODUCING SQUASH — THERAPY

FATHER EASTER in...
What do you mean, Easter is getting Commercial?

FISH PAGE
with FATHER FISHMAS

More fish

I think your comic is ace, but where has the Fish of the Month gone? Please, please, please bring it back, so I can go to my nearest fish shop and buy the Fish of the Month before everybody else does.

Rachel Mathers
Cheadle Hulme

Spawn Again

How can I become a fish? I've tried swimming at the local baths twice a week, holding my breath under water and even eating fish food, but a friend told me that you couldn't become a fish by doing fishworks. What should I do?

D. Page
Ruislip

Unfortunately the world is full of people walking about in their snorkels and flippers who simply cannot accept that they will never be fish. The best I can suggest is to advise them to think happy fish-thoughts.

Ed

Blessed Fishurance

How can I know if I am truly a fish? I like swimming and eating fish food, but I still lack assurance. What do you suggest?

Dotty the Cat
Manchester

See 'Once a fish, always a fish'.

Ed

Fish of the Month

Thank you Claire Imrie for sending in the Fish of the Month – Cod.

Trials and Fish-ulations

Can you help me? I recently became a fish at a Billy Haddock meeting, but when I went back to school the next week and told all my friends, they just laughed at me.

M. Thompson
W. Drayton

Unfortunately no-one ever said being a fish would be easy. In this life we can expect many fish-persecutions. My advice to you is to think constantly about fish-heaven

Ed

Once a Fish, always a Fish

Can you stop being a fish? I have a friend who, until recently, went swimming at the baths every Sunday, said all the right fish-words, and even ate fish food. But now he has gone back to his old squirrel ways. What do you think?

A. Dorrington
Ickenham
Once you are truly spawn again you will always be a fish. But if anyone is in doubt, I suggest a talk with your local fish-monger

Ed

Evangeliwobble

A new dance craze is currently sweeping the nation. Evanjellyfish up and down the country are getting down to the Evangeliwobble. A single by Graham Snedrick, "Do the Evangeliwobble" is currenly No. 1 in the Church-o-teque charts. The dance movements vary according to personal taste and inhibition. You can sway gently with hands raised in the air, or really let your hair down and join in the conga.

Fishword

Down
1. 5 loaves of bread and two ____ (4)
2. Peter the fisherman caught these for a living (4)
3. Dish, spelt wrongly (4)
4. Jonah spent 3 days and 3 nights in the belly of a large one. __ sh (2)

Across
2. Seen swimming in the Lake of Galilee, __sh. (2)
3. Peter's net nearly broke because he caught so many of them (4)
4. SFIH (anagram), (4)
5. If you are blessed you may catch one with a two drachma coin in its mouth (4)

ROBIN MIRE

he's still not on fire

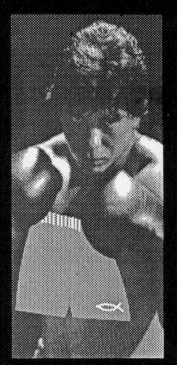

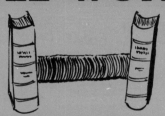

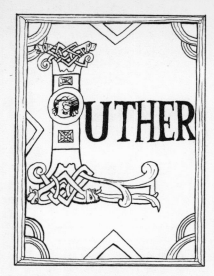

BITS OF THE BODY

* 1 COR. 12:16

INSTRUMENTS OF THE LORD

FISHER OF SOCKS

TROUT

TRENDY

Earlier this year The Trendy Christians completed their sell-out tour of North Humberside church youth clubs. Here we reproduce a selection of lyrics from their latest tape, Live at St. Stephens

(Intro) Hey, just because we're Christians it doesn't mean we can't be trendy. Hit it, 1, 2, 3, 4...

Just because we're Christians
It doesn't mean we can't be trendy
You can still believe in God
And have a fashion sense

Trendy...Christians...
We're trendy...Christians

We like to have a pint of beer
Sometimes we even smoke
We go down the pub and to the disco
And dance to trendy bands

Normal...People
We're normal...People

(intro) Thankyou, thankyou, this next song is called 'Church Isn't Square'...

Church isn't square
It is groovy
Church isn't square
It's cool to be righteous
And we're making it cool to be a Christian

Church is hip
The Bible is interesting
Church is where it's at
We clap and we're not religious
(as it were)

(intro) Yeah, great, this last one is a cover version but we've changed the words slightly...

Hey Mr Normal Christian
With your tambourine
Why don't you go and get your ears pierced?

Hey Mr Normal Christian
Don't be such a stiff
How do you expect to be accepted if you can't dance?

(spoken) Thanks, see you, you've been flipping great. Yeah, flipping, sometimes we even swear.

Matt and Luke Gosspel of The Trendy Christians

THE CALVIN PAGE

with Calvin Stardust

Hello everybody and welcome to the exciting new **CALVIN PAGE** - the page that was **FOREORDAINED** to appear in **WINEBIBBER**. **GREAT!** Now a lot of people will tell you that John Calvin is **BORING**; but we think that's a load of **RUBBISH!** We think Calvin is **FANTASTIC** and you should blow a **BIG RASPBERRY** at anyone who tells you otherwise. Just remember - **CALIVINISM IS FUN!**

"But what is Calvinism and why should I care?" I can hear you ask! **GOOD QUESTION!** John Calvin was a 16th century protestant reformer whose interpretation of **SCRIPTURE** was the flagship of the **REFORMATION. BRILLIANT!**

Space doesn't allow us to go into it too deeply now but just to whet your appetite let's talk about one of the most **INTERESTING** aspects of Calvinism: **PREDESTINATION.** What is it? Simple! First divide the word **PREDESTINATION** into its two parts **PRE** and **DESTINATION.** The **PRE** part implies **BEFOREHAND** and the **DESTINATION** part refers to Man's ultimate destination ie. **HEAVEN** or **HELL**. When the Bible says God *'chose us in him* (Christ) *before the creation of the world...In love he predestined us to be adopted as his sons'* it means (very crudely) that God decided those who would be saved before they were even born.

If you want to find out more about **CALVIN** and **CALVINISM** we suggest you read **CHOSEN BY GOD** by R.C. SPROUL, or , better still, subscribe to **WINEBIBBER** and **WATCH THIS SPACE!**

In this issue of **WINEBIBBER** we've got a fantastic John Calvin story in his native **FRENCH** and lots of exciting **PUZZLES**. What could be more **FUN?!** Next time we'll see how **MAN**, having **SINNED IN ADAM** (Rom 5v12) has lost his **MORAL ABILITY** to **CHOOSE CHRIST** and consequently is a **SLAVE TO SIN** and reliant upon **GOD'S FREELY GIVEN GRACE. BRILLIANT!**

But enough! Time to stop **WAFFLING** and jolly well **GET ON WITH IT!**

Yours in Calvinist's Christian love,

Une bonne storeé de Jean Calvin

Un beau jour d'ete un jeune homme du nom Jean Calvin va a la plage pour jouer avec un bal sur la plage. Quel jour. Le soleil tres chaud et la mer etait tres bleu. Mais, malheureusement, Jean a lance le bal et il a frappe une vielle grandmere sur le nez.

"Oh la la," elle a exclaime.

"Je m'excuse," a dit Jean Calvin.

"Mais non," a dit la grandmere, "C'est juste ma predestination!"

"Pardon?" a repondez Jean, "La predestination, qu'est-ce que c'est?"

"Oh, c'est la decision de God a sauver certaines personnes, mais pas des autres."

"Quelle bonne idee est la predestination! Celui-ci explique beaucoup. Merci vielle grandmere!"

"Comment?" a dit la Grandmere.

Who am I?

My first is in ELECTION but not in PREDESTINATION,

My second is in ATONEMENT but not in LIMITED,

My third is in IRRESISTABLE but not in GRACE,

My fourth is in PERSEVERANCE but not in SAINTS,

My fifth is in DEPRAVITY but not in TOTAL,

My sixth is in SOVEREIGN but not in FREEWILL,

Answer: CALVIN

ANAGRAM

Rearrange the following letters to make up the name of a famous Bible doctrine:

ETSPAONRDIETI

BEHEMOTHS EXTINCT?

EXCLUSIVE

Fourth sighting this month!

A Behemoth has been sighted swimming in Lake Galilee. Holiday-maker Doris Coates sighted the presumed-extinct Bible monster whilst picnicking on the banks of Lake Galilee with her husband.

Said Doris, "I was so surprised I put an extra lump of sugar in my husband's tea." Fortunately, Doris's husband was able to photograph the Behemoth providing us with the most convincing evidence to date for the existence of Behemoths.

U.F.O

However, sceptics have been quick to dismiss the evidence as yet another outrageous publicity stunt by the Israeli Tourist Board. Expert in Strange Things Professor Housenschnitzen, said, "The Behemoth became extinct almost 500 hundred billion years ago this Saturday. It is ludicrous to think that Behemoths are alive and well and swimming about in Lake Galilee. I think the photograph is much more likely to be of a UFO."

Post Office

Meanwhile thousands of Behemoth enthusiasts from around the world have flocked to Lake Galilee in the hope of catching a glimpse of the legendary beast. Ivor Glumph, president of BARDS (Behemoths Are Not Dead Society) said, "This is probably the most significant event in Behemothology since the writing of Job chapter 40."

There has been a dramatic increase in Behemoth sightings in recent years. Only last July Desmond Fox reported seeing a Behemoth come up very close to the Wakefield Post Office where he works, actually come into the shop and buy three first class stamps. Desmond described the Behemoth as mushroom grey in colour, over 40 feet tall and

Early cave painting of a Behemoth playing cards with a Human.

wearing a brown Duffle Coat. Perhaps less well substantiated is the infamous water-skiing Behemoth.

Card Game

The legend of the Behemoth goes back thousands of years. Early cave paintings indicate a close living relationship between Behemoths and Man. But things

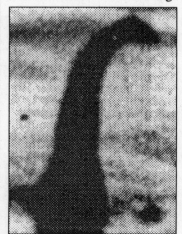

Behemoth in Lake Galilee.

it seems turned sour after a sharp disagreement over a game of cards. From this moment on it appears the Behemoth would

have nothing more to do with human beings and went into hiding; becoming the subject of Man's insatiable curiosity.

Cranks?

Could it then be that Behemoths are finally letting bygones be bygones and slowly emerging from their long years of self-imposed exile? Or is it just that the world is full of cranks? Watch this space for further developments.

CUT-OUT BEHEMOTH
(not life-size)

THE DIVINE PONTIFICATIONS OF ST. AGNES OF CLEVELEYS

All that is known about St.Agnes is that she lived in Cleveleys in the earlier half of this century, and that she read poetry to chickens.

I came to the conclusion of my first pontification as I waited for the tram to Fleetwood. It concerned the whole and the thing contained therein. Wherein the enduring relationship of parts between the material and the immaterial, being aknowledged in tandem to the elementary metaphysical, is one in which we are held in transit of the moment. That is, the essence of the thing itself. Needless to say, the tram conductor did not consider this sufficient reason to let me travel half-fare.

My second pontification occurred as I waited under the drier at 'Perms and Curls'. Love is the shield behind which we wait in patient expectation for the hope in which our faith is contained. This shield should not be lowered, but if it is, we should at least wear shin pads.

The third pontification was not like the others, in that it is indescribable. The message not being contained in words, but in abstract shapes and patterns, rather like Mrs.Dent's carpet at No.10. However, what I can say, is that it concerned the thing itself (see first pontification).

This early photograph captures St.Agnes in classic pose with her shopping.

Top Ten Favourite Chocolate Bars of the Minor Prophets

(last weeks position in brackets).

Not much movement in this weeks charts. Nahum is still number one, but there's a surprise new entry at number three for Amos with a Curly Wurly. Amos tells us, "I've always been a fan of Chocolate bars ever since I was a mini Prophet. Curly Wurlys for me just epitomise all that is good in confectionary; they are interesting, unusual and they have a caramel centre."

1	(1)	Nahum	Crunchie
2	(4)	Obadiah	Milky Way
3	(-)	Amos	Curly Wurly
4	(2)	Micah	Mars
5	(6)	Joel	Behemoth Bar
6	(5)	Zechariah	Kit-Kat
7	(8)	Zephaniah	Twirl
8	(9)	Malachi	Twix
9	(3)	Jonah	Whispa
10	(7)	Habakkuk	Peppermint Aero

Archbishop Cliff

The next Archbishop of Cantebury will be Cliff Richard, the General Synod announced yesterday. The 50 year old pop singer was the obvious choice for the top job in the Anglican Church. Jean Matthews, Sunday school teacher at St. Mary's Church, Chingford, said that Cliffs appointment would prove to the world that Christians are not boring. She also revealed that Cliff would probably not give up his musical career, and that the ' swinging Bishop' would be touring early next year.

Cliff Richard was unavailable for comment, but Jean Matthews said that the appointment would lead to many more pop stars in leadership positions.

The next Archbishop?

PROPHECY COLUMN

In the third verse of the fourth chapter of the book of Leviticus, I did fall into a deep sleep and I did dream dreams as it was foretold.

And an angel did appear unto me saying, "Mortal man, harken thou unto me for thou must take this message unto all mankind." And the angel did thence speak unto me and I took notes. Here is what he said:

"In the last days there will be much confusion, leaky pipes and generally a lot of bad plumbing. And many plumbers shall be called, and the number of the plumbers shall be nine times ninety-nine times nine-hundred and ninety-nine times...(well anyway, let's face it, there'll be a lot). And the many plumbers will not know how to fix the leaky pipes and one will break a fingernail trying.

"And then there will be seven minutes of tribulation and Mrs Watson's milk will boil over. For the first three and a half minutes she will be on the phone, but for the second three and a half minutes she will notice and turn off the stove.

"And there will be ten rucksacks and ten sleeping bags and the ten sleeping bags will have to be rolled up very tightly if they are to fit inside the ten rucksacks and leave enough room for other things.

"And around this time a man will appear whose shoes are too tight and he will go to get them mended. But in the shoe repairers he will be eaten by a beast with six heads and he will not be very happy about it."

Thus endeth the prophecy.

ROBIN O'MIRE

CLERGY CLOSE-UP

Name: Alan Stevens

Position: Reverend

Church: St. Rogers

Diocese: Cumbria

Age: 48

Height: 5' 8"

Weight: 11st. 2lb

Previous Churches:
St. Philips, Norwich

No. church appearances: 765

Which person would you most like to meet: Robert Runcie

Favourite Clothes: Dog Collar

International collars:
Church of England vs. Vatican

Favourite Food: Communion

Favourite Hymn: Amazing Grace

Best Country visited: Israel

Favourite book: Bible

Favourite T.V. show:
Songs of Praise

Favourite Musician:
Graham Snedrick

What would you like to be if you weren't a vicar: Astronaut

Miscellaneous likes:
When sermons go well

Miscellaneous dislikes:
Yawning in church

The SACRED
Diary of Robin Mire *(age 22¹/2)*

Saturday 3rd April

Feel led to keep a log. I found one at the bottom of the garden. I will keep it beside my moss collection.

Sunday 4th April

Very long and boring sermon in church today. A record three-course meal talk. When someone shouted 'Amen' I spilt my lasagne into the collection plate. Still, all goes to a good cause I suppose.

Monday 5th April

Aren't some of the things we do and say as Christians faintly ridiculous. I'm often left clutching my sides helpless with laughter yet moved by the genuine affection which holds us all together.

Tuesday 6th April

The church asked me to join in their corny praise march today. I said I hated praise marches, then I said they should do a 'praise jog' or a 'praise hop'. No-one laughed. I think they hate me.

Wednesday 7th April

Went to see 'The Last Temptation of Christ' to see what all the fuss is about. Someone with a 'Smile Jesus Loves You' sticker tried to stop me getting in. Couldn't be bothered telling him I was a Christian. Some new people moved in next door today, I wonder what they're like?

Thursday 8th April

The new man next door is the same person who tried to stop me going to see the film yesterday. He's an evangelical with slightly charismatic leanings.

Friday 9th April

Went to the pub for a drink with non-Christians. A lady wearing a 'Smile Jesus Loves You' badge tried to witness to me. She didn't believe I was a Christian. She said I didn't look like one!

Saturday 10th April

Amazing. The new lady who lives next door is the same lady who tried to witness to me in the pub last night. She speaks a new kind of language - half-English / half-Bible. She came round to borrow some tea-bags. I gave her a whole packet hoping she wouldn't have to come back for a long time. She said I was very generous and that I must be very close to the Lord!

Sunday 11th April

Didn't want to get rebuked in church again so I paid extra special attention during the sermon. It was about prayer (just for a change). We were told we don't pray enough, when you don't feel like praying that's exactly when you should pray, he's not just interested in the big things, he's interested in the little things aswell, why worry when you can pray?, you can't put God in a box, and, don't sing this chorus if you don't mean it. I had a cliche attack and raised my feet during worship for a joke. Mrs. Benson said to me, "If you don't mind me saying, it's no wonder you don't get anything out of the service when you don't put anything in." It's true I don't get anything out of the service, but how does she know? And what exactly is it you're supposed to put in? Now I'll hold a grudge against her for weeks. Why didn't she just say I was annoying her? I'm sure God hates me.

Monday 12th April

I don't know why I bother going to church sometimes.

Tuesday 13th April

Mrs. Benson caught me on the way home from work and asked me to help her with some gardening. She was wondering why she hadn't had many tulips this year, then she wondered whether she'd remembered to put any bulbs in. I said, "If you don't put anything in, how can you expect to get anything out?" She laughed, it sort of broke the ice but I was really just trying to be nasty.

Wednesday 14th April

I saw Sandra from church on the bus on the way home tonight. I told her all about my moss collection. Judging by her expression I think she must have been fascinated.

Thursday 15th April

I'm in love. I've been thinking about Sandra all day. She can borrow my tea-bags anytime.

Friday 16th April

Sandra, Sandra, Sandra. She probably hates me.

Saturday 17th April

I'm always falling in love and nothing ever happens.

Sunday 18th April

Sandra wasn't in church today. In fact church was virtually empty. Everyone had gone to the Spring Jumpers Praise thrash for their special Easter emotions. I can picture them all now, screwing up their faces 'meaning it' when they take communion. Old Mrs. Thompson brought a basket of wheat to our service thinking it was the Harvest Thanksgiving service. I suppose she meant well, but I just thought the corn was corny. While the vicar was doing his sermon on 'God still speaks', the phone rang in his office. Everyone thought this was highly amusing, except me. I thought the phone was phoney. Even the sellotape holding the Spring Harvest poster up was tacky.

Monday 19th April

I decided to read my Bible - for the first time in a week. I chose my favourite book - Job.

Tuesday 20th April

I've had quiet times two days in a row now. I'm turning into a Super-Christian, I'm walking in The Victory!

Wednesday 21st April

Sandra doesn't want me. I heard off a friend of a friend. Sometimes life is just one downer after another. Oh dear, I can feel another quench coming on. Goodnight Diary.

Let the women remain silent in church.

Kevin Bumble, he's so humble.

Larry Normal.

The long dark night of the sole.

God answered our prayer with a score draw, although personally I would have preferred a win.

Never mind, we can rest assured God has his reasons. All St. Stephens can do is to play in faith, and besides, with God on our side we're always winners, in a sense.

Meanwhile, in the home of St. Stephen's chairman, Elton Charlton

~ deep joy ~

...And finally, Sin City 1, St. Stephens 1, making a total of 12 score draws.

Hallelujah! I've won the pools! £750,000, that'll fund the St. Stephens Evangelistic Missionary Football Outreach to Brazil!

Gazing into the guidance ball with Rustling Grant... PROPHECY-SCOPES

22 DEC – 19 JAN
You will feel led to discover God's will for your life (as you have done every January for the past five years).

20 JAN – 18 FEB
You really feel the Lord is saying you should buy 'Leading and Guidance' by Herman Neutics, and then feel led to put the five points into practise.

19 FEB – 20 MAR
You feel the Lord is asking you to buy an orange bomber jacket for your Great Aunt Ethel for her birthday, and then feel disappointed when she shows no gratitude.

21 MAR – 19 APRIL
Your dog's lead snaps and you feel led to buy a new one.

20 APRIL – 20 MAY
You pray for guidance and feel led to attend the local praise march but are suddenly forced to leave when you feel led to throw up.

21 MAY – 21 JUNE
Feel led to go on holiday. This will then be confirmed when the vicar asks you where you are going on holiday this year.

22 JUNE – 22 JULY
You will feel led to smash up your friends Led Zeppelin collection, but don't be surprised if he feels led to punch your face in.

23 JULY – 22 AUG
Feel led to think again about issues concerning God's leading.

23 AUG – 22 SEPT
Generally trying to feel led and guided this month, and generally failing.

23 SEPT – 22 OCT
You will begin to doubt and feel cynical about trying to listen for 'leadings'. You tell your pastor and he points out (rather unhelpfully) that God is leading you through a time of testing.

23 OCT – 21 NOV
This month you will feel led to throw a hymn book at the vicar during his sermon entitled 'God's Guidance: Three handy pointers' but resist and choose to fall asleep instead.

22 NOV – 21 DEC
Feel led to throw your book by Herman Neutics in the bin and decide to buy 'Decision Making and the Will of God' by Gary Friesen and J. Maxson (published by Multnomah) instead.

BOOK REVIEW
by Donald Fenn

Good Grief, *the story of Charles Shultz,* Rheta Grimsley Johnson, *Ravette,* £7.99.

This is a good book.
★★★

And the Beagles and the Bunnies Shall Lie down Together, *the theology in Peanuts,* Charles Schultz, *Ravette,* £2.95.

So is this.
★★★

The Bible, Moses et all, *Hodder and Stoughton,* £7.95

Absolutely brilliant! Inspired! Apparently this book is centuries old, but don't let that put you off. There's something for everybody here, including poetry, wisdom and the law. Those with a particular interest in Jewish History should also find this book immensely revealing. Although a little long and tedious in places, I can't recommend it enough. Could become a classic.
★★★★★★★★★★★★

Do not get...
DRUNK ON WINE

SNEDFISH

Exclusive Interview with Graham Snedrick

We interviewed Graham Snedrick recently on the opening night of his sell-out Evangeliwobble Tour, in Plymouth. The gig was a huge success by all measures, and afterwards we tried to find out a little bit more about this charismatic figure.

Winebibber: Graham, the show was a great success.

Graham: Yes it was, I felt very warm and fuzzy tonight and I think the audience picked up on that.

We haven't seen you for a long while, not since your praise march, what have you been up to?

Well I've been in the studio writing and recording some new choruses, and just really trying to relax.

Yes I bet all that marching took it out of you!?

Well yes it did. Ha ha ha. You have to be very fit to really worship God. Those somersaults and flip-flops are really tiring.

Are there plans for any more in the way of praise marches?

Yes, in fact just today, being here in Plymouth, I was talking to a naval captain down there on the docks, about the possibility of a praise-swim. It'll be an opportunity for plenty of synchronised praise-swimming, underwater repentance and raising flippers. We'll also be building a giant replica of the large fish that swallowed Jonah, because it wasn't a whale of course, it was a fish.

Sounds different.

Just really different, and we all feel very warm and fuzzy about it.

Where and when can we expect to see...er...this?

Hopefully this summer, all going well, when the weather's nice. At most holiday resorts and a few swimming pools around the country. It'll be an opportunity to witness to tourists and holiday makers, and fish.

Fish?

Yes, we really just feel that our Lord's command to be fishers has been neglected too often and we really just want to put that right.

Surely the command is to be fishers of men, not fish?

Both I think. I'm a very good friend of Father Fishmas. In a sense we are all fish.

Er...yes, well moving on, about your new songs?

I've got a new single out soon. We were messing around in the studio the other week and I started playing this happy little jolly tune and I thought, "That's nice, now I just need some words." And I thought "What could I sing along to this?" and I decided to use the words of Leviticus.

Leviticus?

Yes, you know, wave offerings and meat sacrifices, all that sort of thing.

That's an unusual subject for a chorus.

I think so but I felt that recently my lyrics had been getting a bit too lightweight. I just really feel that the time is right to move into something that's a bit heavier. My ambition is to write a musical based on Louis Berkhof's 'Systematic Theology'

Let's talk about your early influences and experiences

Yes, certainly. Interestingly I feel that a lot of my work is in fact a reaction against my early childhood experience. I remember my mother used to force me against my will to memorise and recite hymns by Charles Wesley. I suppose I have reacted against that by writing hymns that would be easy to memorise. I was given my first guitar for my eighth birthday. I learned very quickly. Within three months I could play 'When I Survey the Wondrous Cross' using my teeth; you know, all that Jimi Hendrix stuff. But my church didn't like it, they threw me out of the worship group. I can't remember what denomination they were; I think they were Ophthalmologists. They wouldn't even let you raise a suggestion, never mind a fin, I mean an arm.

Sounds like you didn't fit in.

I felt very out of place right from the very start. When I was attending Sunday School creche I tried to organise a praise-toddle for the under-2's. But the teachers found out about it and quickly put a stop to it. I always felt somewhat different from the other kids. My mother says I could speak in tongues before I could speak in English, "Goo, goo, ga, ga."

So when exactly was it that you decided you wanted to be a fish?

It was while I was at college studying Marine Psychology. A group of us students used to stay up late discussing trout. Then one of them invited me along to the local swimming baths one day, and eventually I decided to take the plunge.

And how has this new life affected you?

The thing that a lot of people don't realise is that being a fish isn't easy. There is a lot of misunderstanding, this can result in mockery or even aggression. But for those of us who are determined to swim up the narrow stream to Fish-Heaven, they are obstacles which we are happy to...I'm sorry, are you laughing?

No, no, just clearing my throat here. I think I have a cold coming on.

Oh dear, I'm sorry to hear that. But, as I was saying, it isn't all plain-swimming, there are many fish-persecutions, but it's going to be worth it when we receive those fish-crowns. That's a nasty cough you have there. Are you sure I can't get you something, a glass of water maybe?

No, no, I'll be fine. Thanks for the interview.

My pleasure.

Leviticus by Graham Snedrick

If the offering is to be a burnt offering
Oh then it must be a male without defect
And if the offering is to be a grain offering
Well then it really must just be of fine flour

Oh let's just offer them, offer them
Being careful not to break the Levitical code
Come on let's offer them, offer them
(male singers) And give your hands a good clean afterwards
(female singers) Use plenty of soap and water

Well if you can't afford to bring a lamb
Then bring two doves or pigeons instead
And if you can't afford to bring these birds
Then a tenth of an epaph of fine flour will do

And then just offer them, offer them
And remember some of the offering's the priest's
Well come on let's offer them, offer them
(male part) And learn the origin of the term 'scapegoat'
(female part) Ooh that's interesting

Everyone's invited to the Feast of Trumpets
Though even my commentary isn't sure what it's about
And everyone's welcome at the Feast of weeks
But don't forget to bring an offering (informal wear)

Well some people aren't really sure what to do
But that's OK the Tabernacle information Desk are keen to help

Graham Snedrick

A TIME TO LAUGH...

For a little light relief, the Winebibber offers you a HUMOROUS page of FUNNY prayer cards!

Fishprints

One night I had a dream. I was swimming alongside the beach when I noticed a set of fishprints in the sand. I looked further along the beach and I saw Gerald walking erect upon his hind flippers. I was just about to ask him what in Darwin's name he was doing when he turned into a pterodactyl and flew away. I just shrugged my fins and thought, "Oh well, that's evolution for you!"

Prayer for everything

Lord, please help everyone, everywhere, whatever they're doing.

Amen.

Prayer for a black leather jacket

O Lord, please send my way a black leather jacket.

Amen.

Prayer for a better crop of tomatoes

O Lord, please may my garden yield a more bountiful and more succulent crop of tomatoes this year.

Amen.

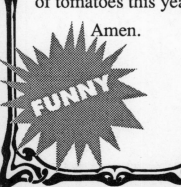

Footprints in my dad's freshly laid cement

One night I had a dream. I was running home from school very fast. I ran down my road, turned quickly into my garden and headed for the front door. Little did I know that my dad had just been cementing our front path that very afternoon. Anyway, I soon noticed that although the upper half of my body was still running, the bottom half was completely stationary. I looked down and saw that my feet were firmly embedded in my dad's freshly laid cement. I couldn't move an inch! I was just about to start crying when I woke up and found that my little brother had tied up my feet in his towel and was jumping up and down on my bed playing Cowboys and Indians!

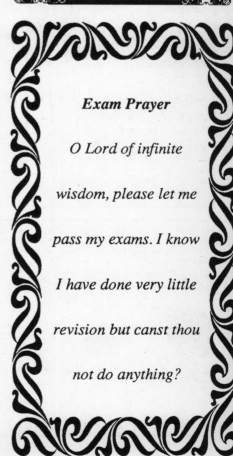

Exam Prayer

O Lord of infinite wisdom, please let me pass my exams. I know I have done very little revision but canst thou not do anything?

NiGEL the BAPTiST

Proverb: 'Tis a foolish man that keepeth fish in his underpants

The following is a reconstruction, using actors, of a real incident that took place recently. The victim wishes to remain anonymous.

This, and thousands of similar incidents demonstrate all too well that no-one can be sure when a zap will strike. But what are we to make of this warm and fuzzy phenomenon? We interviewed Derek Spaggis, father of two and by all accounts a strictly hands down Christian. This is his story...

Derek is currently recovering in intensive care recovering from a serious bout of Joy of the Lord. Should we believe his story? If so, what are we to make of these warm and fuzzy creatures? Our investigations continue...

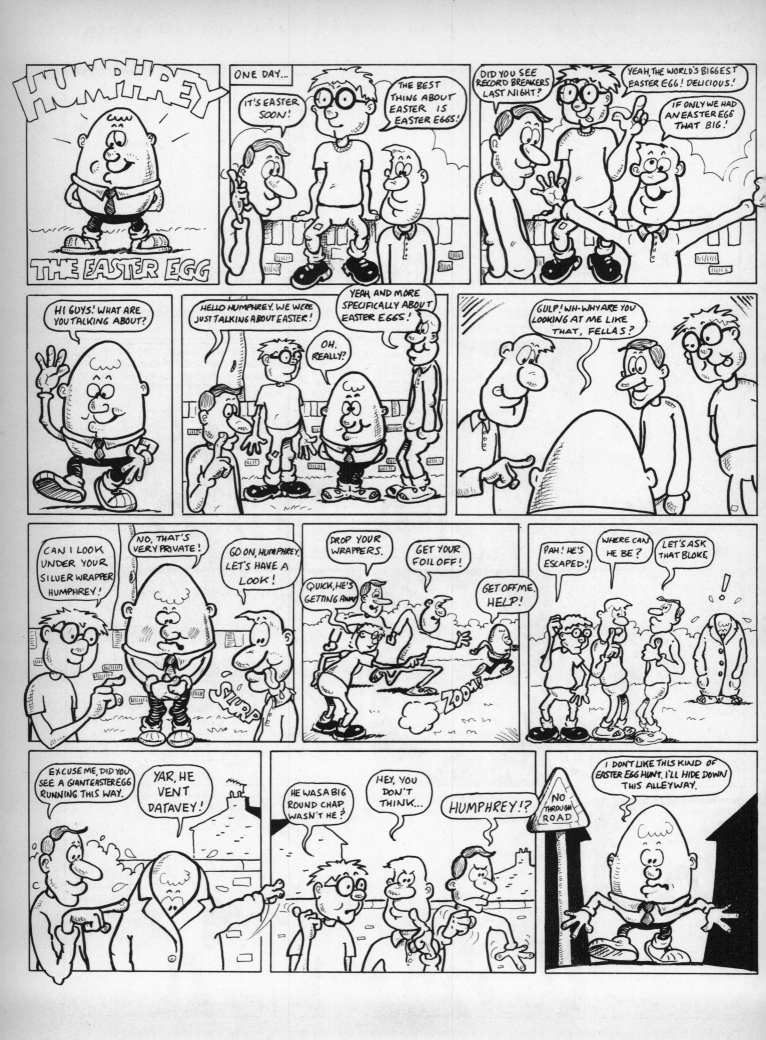

Humphrey Dumphrey sat on a wall
Humphrey Dumphrey raised his hands and fell
All the Kings horses and all the Kings men
Laid hands on Humphrey to heal him again

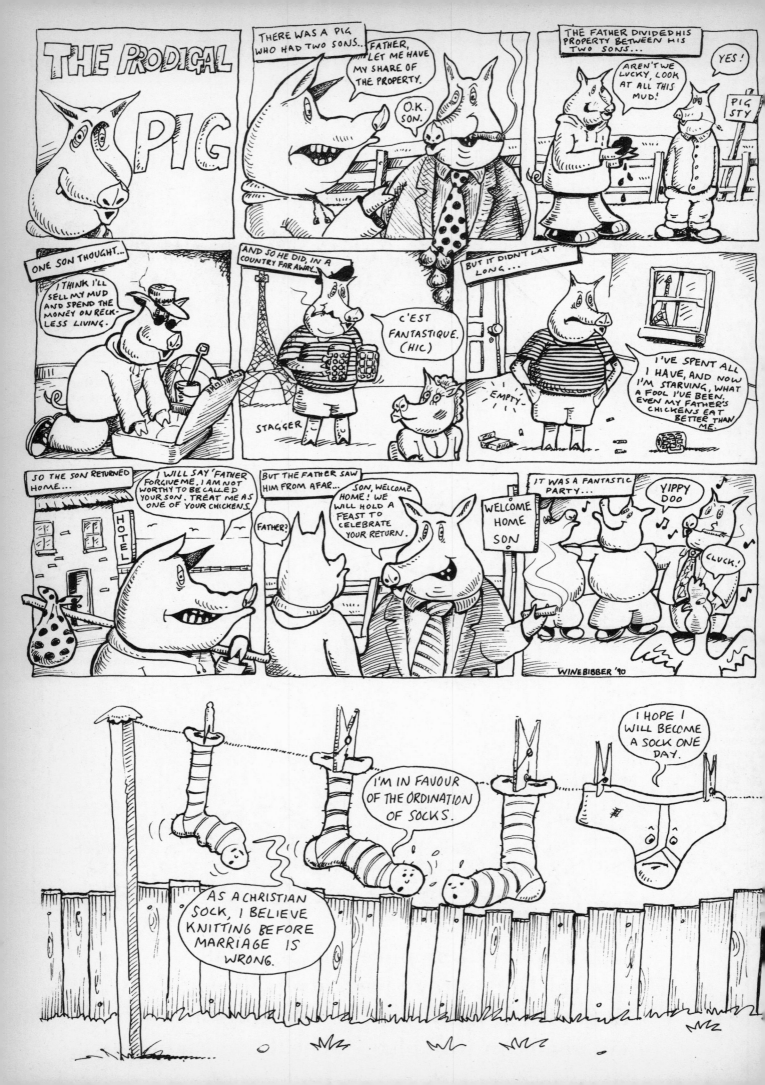

PARABLES IN PERSPECTIVE - "MIDNIGHT CALLER"

ROBIN MIRE
not on fire at the Houseparty

PASTOR PAT
and his black and white Bible

Pat and Amos have called at Granny Wesley's for a cup of **tea.**

Granny is knitting a hymn book. Amos likes **the** look of her wool.

Amos plays with the ball of wool while Granny and Pat discuss hermeneutics.

"So you adhere to the doctrine of **Arminianism**?" says Pat.

"How else can I come to terms with the paradox of **man's free will** and **God's sovereign election**," says Granny.

"Surely **Rom 3v12** tells us that man has lost the **moral ability** to **choose salvation**," exegetes Pat.

"That's out of context," screams Granny, angrily waving her knitting needles in a slightly charismatic way.

"Look Amos is tied up in the wool; just like we are tied up in theological exposition," laughs Pat.

WHAT'S UP, VIC?

Reverend Gerald Smith retires this week after fifteen years as the Vicar of St. Vincent's, Hull. The unusual thing about Gerald is that he is a sock. I asked Gerald about his life at St. Vincent's.

Rev. Sock: Overall I have enjoyed it. Obviously, it has not been without difficulty. St Vincent's is a very traditional parish and for a long time I struggled against a lot of anti-sock feelings, particularly prejudice against the ordination of socks. I'm glad to say, that has all disappeared now. In fairness, I can see how it may have appeared to some to be rather peculiar, having a sock as a vicar. But I think that was largely an expression of pride – the idea that it is somehow demeaning to be preached at by an item of footwear. What a lot of people don't realise is that a lot of famous Christians in history were in fact socks. John Wesley, for example, was a sock.

Winebibber: I suspect you must have found being the vicar of a church named after St Vincent somewhat ironic?

S: (laughs) Yes. Not a lot of people realise that St Vincent is that the patron saint of Socks!

W: What do you think the Church of England should be doing at the moment?

S: I think it is doing a good job, but I do feel very angry that socks are ignored when it comes to evangelism. We often hear sermons about witnessing to our neighbours or our workmates, but when, oh, when do we receive good instruction concerning the evangelisation of socks? St Vincent's is making some progress in this area by having special 'Bring a sock' evenings. They are informal evenings in which members of our congregation are able to bring socks they know to a Christian meeting, without having the stigma of it being a 'church' event. We have picnics, country-dancing, darning, all sorts of things.

W: And how successful have they been?

S: Well so far we haven't had any actual conversions, but a pair of tights has been asking some very deep questions.

W: I understand you are also heavily involved with 'Sock Off' – the Campaign for Sock Rights?

S: Yes, it's a simple question of rights. How would you like to be worn a foot all your life and then just thrown out or used as a duster? We are looking to open up more of our Homes for Elderly Socks, youth clubs for teenage socks, and so on. Places where socks can go and relax and, perhaps more importantly, where they can meet other socks whom they can understand and relate to regarding the many issues we face as footwear. Incidentally, I use the word sock because of its common usage, but we are in fact, more accurately speaking, woolly feet gloves.

W: You have been criticised for placing too much emphasis on the role of socks rather than that of people.

S: Yes, I hear that. I suppose that because I am a sock I naturally look at life from the point of view of a sock. I do think, however, that deep down beneath the surface, socks and people are in fact the same. We are all, in a sense, looking for something. Some humans look for it in expensive cars. Some socks look for it in expensive shoes. I think it is only when we are willing to face up to our inner knitwear that we can truly begin to find the answers. I think we are all called to be washers of each others' socks.

W: Reverend Sock, thank you.

S: Thank you.

Rev. Gerald Smith relaxing 'out-of-shoe'

 The legendary final issue of Winebibber comic (issue No.8); £1.25 (U.K.), £2.50 (overseas), prices include p&p. Send cheques payable to 'Winebibber Publications' - 21 Marlborough Ave., Cheadle Hulme, Cheshire, SK8 7AP, England.